To Grandma-Mother Rose
whose Life Ship is full of love and always ready to welcome you aboard.

I want to thank all the crew members on my Life Ship that have inspired,
guided, and supported me on my life journey!

Published by:

PH2E VENTURES
www.iouliving.com

PH2E, IOU Living - IOU Life Leadership, IOU Life Map Cycle, and SelfCulture are registered trademarks of
Dr. Joe Famularo

ISBN 979-8-9868289-0-9 (hardcover)
ISBN 979-8-9868289-1-6 (paperback)
ISBN 979-8-9868289-2-3 (e-book)

Library of Congress Control Number 2022916174

MY IOU LIFE SHIP – *Get ready for the Journey!* is distributed worldwide.
For more information and lessons associated with this book visit www.iouliving.com.

MY IOU LIFE SHIP

Get ready for the Journey!

By the author of the bestseller *IOU Life Leadership*

DR. JOE FAMULARO

Illustrated by Vytautas Bikauskas

PH2E VENTURES
New York

We are all like a Ship,
That floats on the sea.
Getting ready for our journey,
of what our lives can be.

Is your Life Ship ready?
You must prepare it well.
It's time to hoist your anchor,
and give a heartfelt farewell.

The joy on this journey,
you'll surely never forget.
Like that first year of school,
when you learned the alphabet.

Turning the captain's wheel,
I'm sailing on my own.
My family's in my heart,
so I'm not really alone.

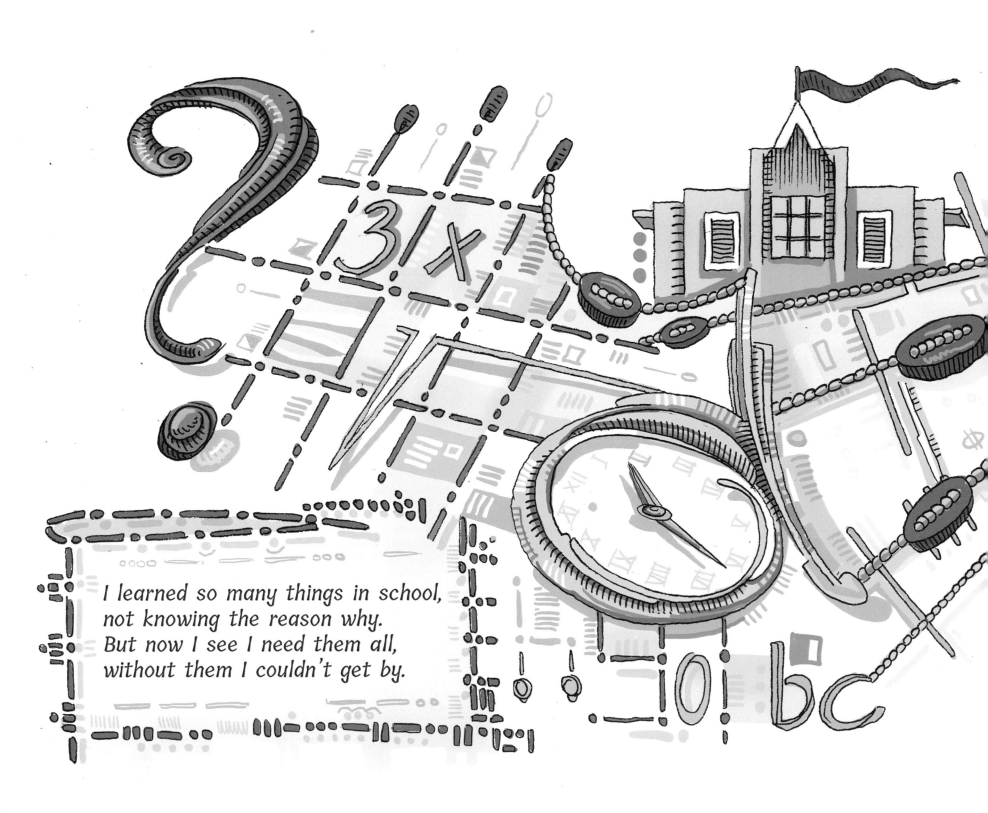

I learned so many things in school,
not knowing the reason why.
But now I see I need them all,
without them I couldn't get by.

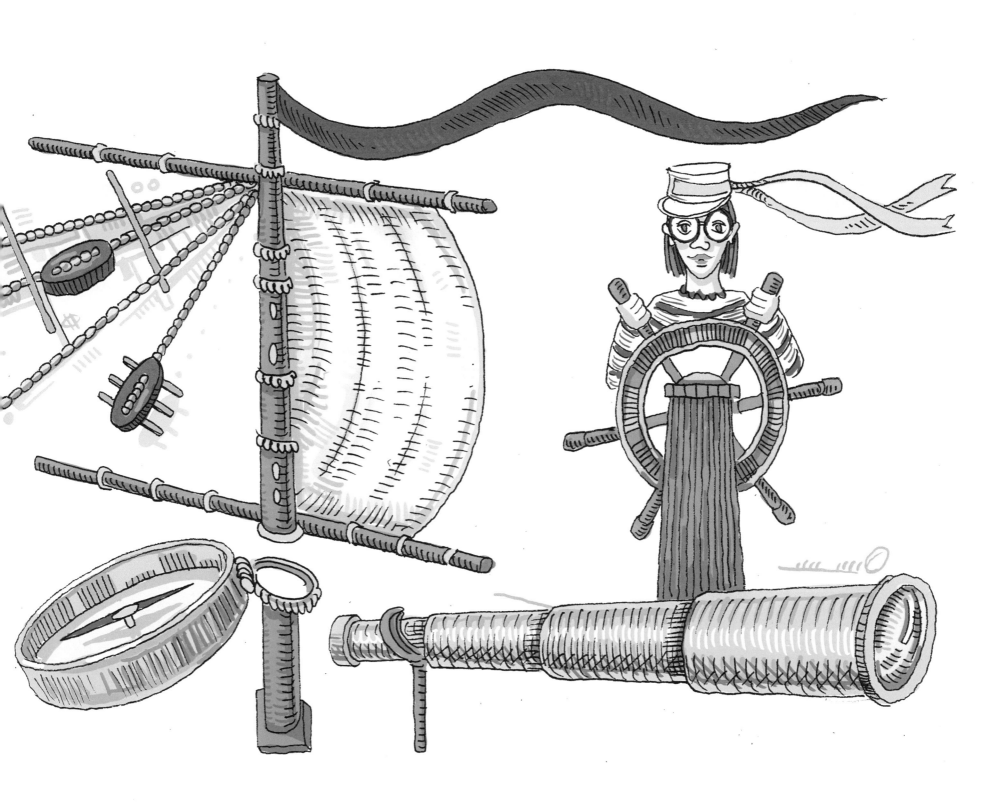

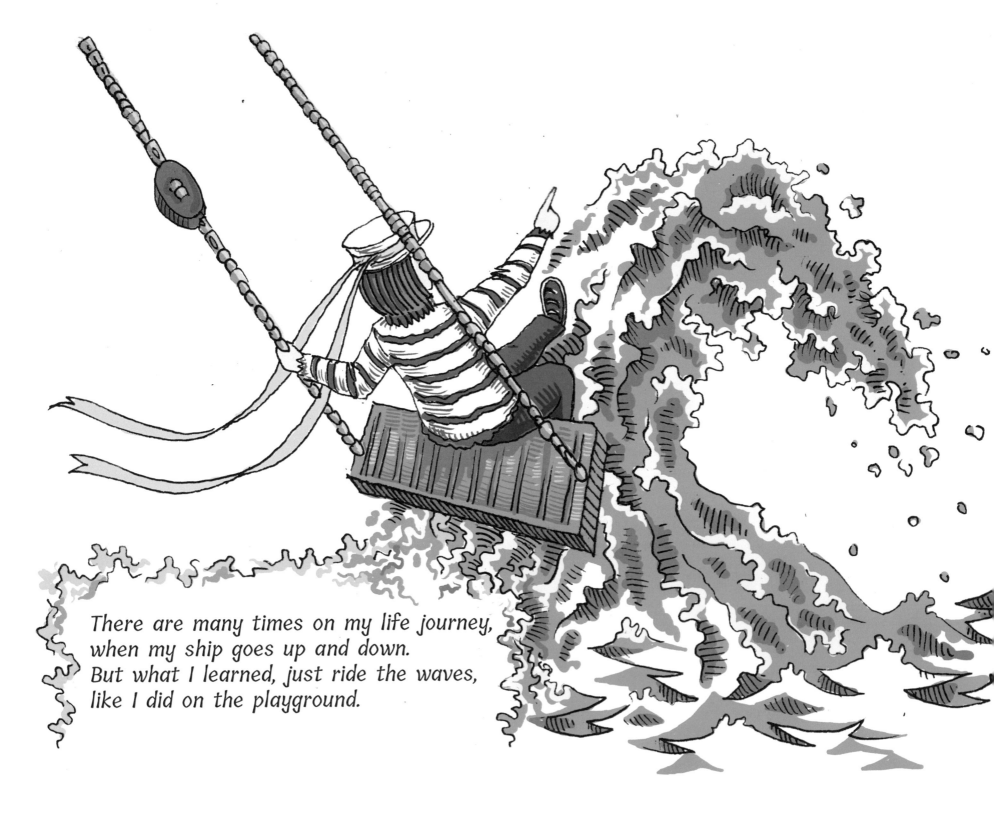

There are many times on my life journey,
when my ship goes up and down.
But what I learned, just ride the waves,
like I did on the playground.

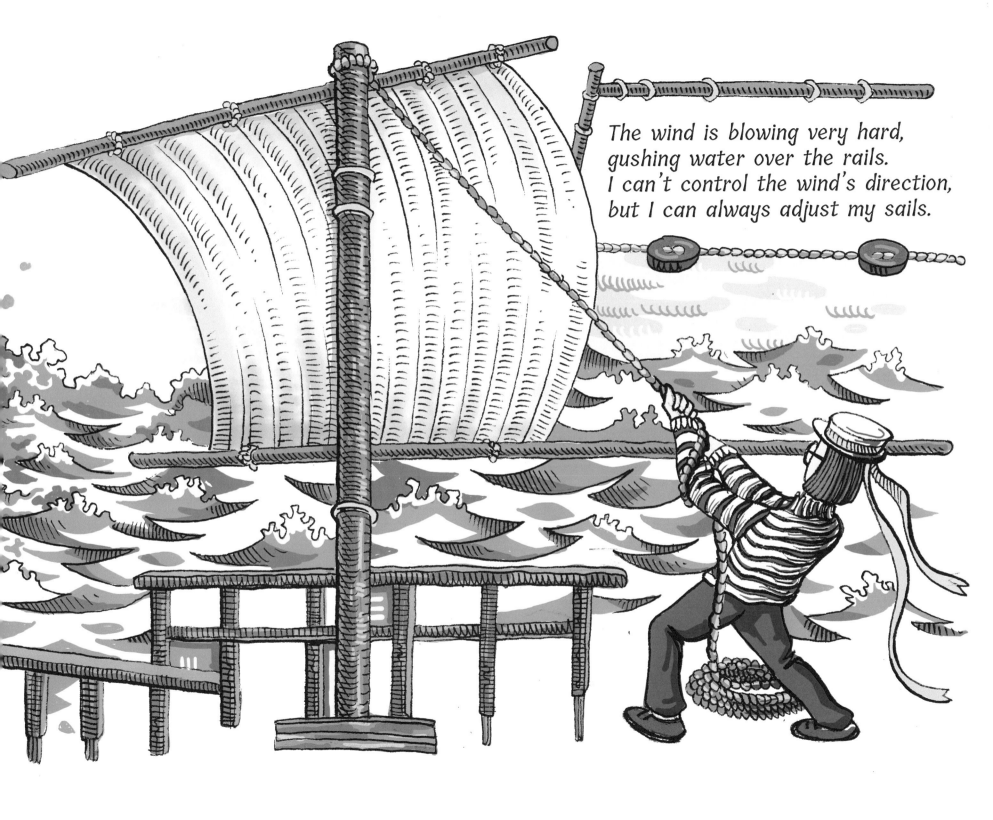

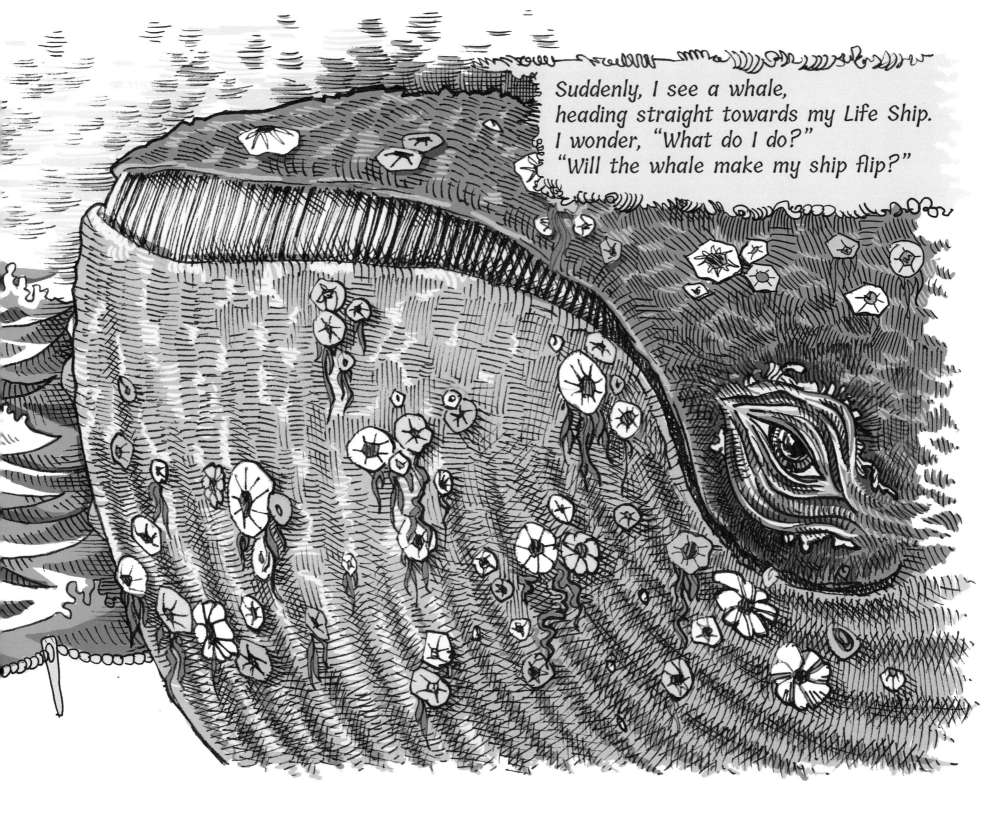

I said, "Thank you, my friend,
for helping me get through this time."
"You gave me so much confidence,
now I'm ready to climb."

So, I turned my sails,
pointed up to the sky.
Let's see if the I.O.U.,
is ready to sail fast and fly.

The world looks so different up here,
it changed my point of view.
The people, the water, the land,
everything looks so brand new.

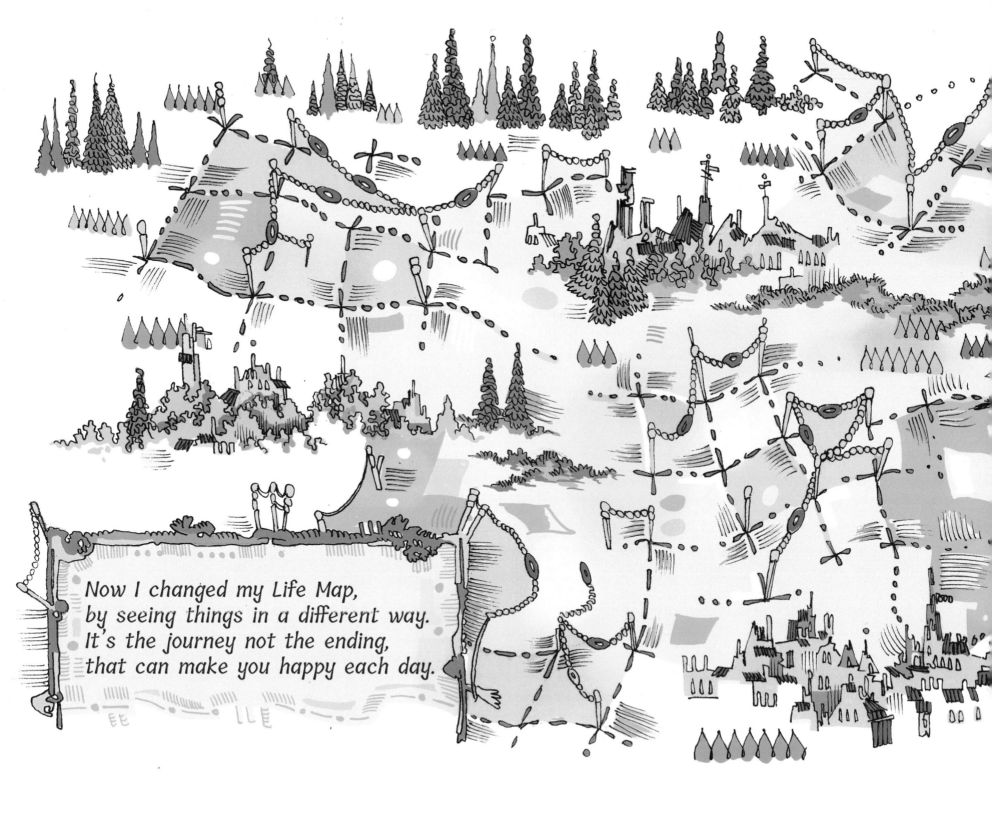

Now I changed my Life Map,
by seeing things in a different way.
It's the journey not the ending,
that can make you happy each day.

I learned so much on this journey,
full of excitement and fun.
Oh, I can't wait to sail home,
and share my tales with everyone.

Your life's an amazing journey,
that begins like a little seed.
Many others will help it grow,
but you're the Captain, so take the lead.

MY IOU LIFE SHIP

Author's Notes

You are the Captain of your Life Ship. Is it on course, drifting, or even sinking?
This book is a child's companion to the bestseller, *IOU Life Leadership*,
which is a foundational framework based on timeless, universal principles,
for positive and effective intentional living from the inside out
to help keep your Life Ship on course.

Throughout this picture book, key IOU principles and concepts are introduced
in child-friendly language. The following *Author's Notes* offer insightful
background information for the adult reader.
They may be used for further teaching, learning,
and discussions for each page of the book.

Be selective and explain only those which are related to your goals for the listener(s).

Scenes 1, 2:

Our lives are all like a ship on a journey carrying many gifts and talents already inside us (represented by the stack of boxes on the ship) that make us uniquely who we are. I call this our Inward Self, the foundation of our Life Ship. Our Inward Self is our thoughts, feelings, and character – everything we are that we take with us and use on our journeys through life.

To succeed in keeping our Life Ship on course, we need to prepare well – learn and practice skills and strategies, continually acquire new knowledge, set goals, and gain important social-emotional skills such as being able to handle change and unexpected events. Then we lift our anchor, push off and begin our journey towards our life dreams. The challenge is to keep our Inward Self (the boxes on the ship) balanced during the events we encounter during our life journeys.

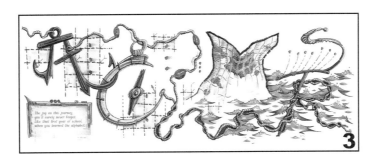

Scene 3:

Every journey holds many unexpected sources of joy. When we are unsure of ourselves or in the midst of challenges, it's good to think about past successful and happy journeys. Find at least 9 letters in the illustration recalling the listeners' journey learning letters. Share that on each journey there can be something new and exciting to learn.

Scene 4:

The most fundamental concept is **IOU – Inward Outward Upward** – renamed for children as **Inside Outside Up**. Inward (Inside us) refers to our Inward Self – everything that makes us who we are. It is our Inward thoughts and intentions, our Inward being, our Inward life maps, life experiences and thoughts since we were born. Outward (Outside us) refers to our Outward relationships and interactions with other people, living things, and the outside world. Upward (Up) refers to Upward Living that we strive to receive which is the byproduct based on how we live Inwardly and Outwardly. It's moving towards a dynamic positive culture for ourselves (SelfCulture™) and others.

When we are well prepared and living positively and effectively, our Life Ship is on course, and we receive the Upward Living Life Gifts of *Peacefulness*, *Happiness*, *Healthiness*, and *Excellence* – what I call our **PH2E**. Receiving **PH2E** is Upward Living that helps us grow. Chant and act out the IOU hand signs with the listener(s).

Scenes 5, 6:

We should recognize our closest family and friends who support our journeys, known on our Life Ship as our crew. We should listen to them when they encourage us to follow our dreams. They can give us confidence to begin and continue new undertakings. They are always inside us even when they are physically distant from us during our life journeys. After recognizing the people on our Life Ship and discovering the dreams inside us, it is important to set goals. Then, we should take that outward first step, even though we may feel nervous excitement about the journey ahead. Ask the listener(s) to list the people who are on their Life Ship.

Scene 7:

Our past Inward and Outward experiences help guide us on our current journey. Sometimes, we might not even understand why we need to learn certain things in school and at home. Later, we are enlightened to see how they clearly connect and help us to be successful on our journey, moving towards excellence. Can you and the listener(s) think of skills you are currently learning that might be helpful in the future?

Scenes 8, 9:

Our previous experiences of difficulties and change can help us as we navigate the present. For example, outward challenges, disruption, and change will always be part of life – in fact we often have no control over what causes them.

We should focus on what we have 100% control over – our Inward thoughts, decisions, and reflection on previous actions and experiences, rather than what we have no control over – the thoughts, decisions, and actions of others. Focusing inwardly on what we have control over will help us navigate those challenging moments while keeping our "boxes" balanced.

Scenes 10, 11, 12:

Situations are not always what they seem to be at first glance. What might seem like a threat or danger may in fact be something that helps us. It's important not to jump to any conclusions but first take in and see all the data we can before making judgments and decisions based on them. This is the first stage, "See" of the IOU Life Map Cycle for Kids™. Once we take in the data, we organize it in the "Think" stage, then create a plan in the "Decide" stage and finally implement it in the "Act" stage. The captain's internal Life Map perspective of the whale changed based on reflection at each stage of the Life Map Cycle for Kids™. The captain observed all the data from the whale's words and actions ("See" stage). Then thought about the data that was observed ("Think" stage). Next, the captain decided to trust the whale and sail together, and after gaining confidence from their meeting, decided to see if the IOU Life Ship could sail to the sky ("Decide" stage). Finally, the captain acted on the decisions by sailing with the whale, and in the next scene sailing the ship to the sky ("Act" stage). For more information on *The Life Map Cycle for Kids*™, go to *ioulessons.com*

Scenes 13, 14:

Taking in all the information about our outward encounters and experiences with others can help broaden our perspectives which then gives us new knowledge and confidence. These new skills help us to take risks (the captain seeing if their ship can fly), which can change our points of view and let us see things in a new and different way. This, in turn, helps us make better decisions and plans for the next journey by updating our internal Life Maps and then using the Life Map Cycle for Kids™ again.

Scene 15:

We learn that *Peacefulness*, *Happiness*, *Healthiness*, and *Excellence* (PH2E) are found along the way, not just when we reach our goal or destination. PH2E are the byproducts of staying on course, focusing on being positive and effective, and enjoying each moment throughout our life journeys. Remember, when you receive PH2E, you are Upward Living.

Scenes 16, 17, 18:

Our lives are a series of journeys, and we are in charge of each one of them. You decide where to go and set goals on how to get there. Make sure to use all the tools that you already have inside you to navigate through the calm and storms to keep your Life Ship on course. We share our journeys with our family and friends, and they can provide important help and support along the way towards our dreams and goals. Yet, the journey and the choices are ultimately yours, so remember you are the captain of your IOU Life Ship, take the helm, set your course, and begin your journey!

There are additional life leadership analogies hidden throughout this book.
Have fun discovering them with your listener(s).
For example: What might the ribbon on the captain's hat represent?

For detailed IOU Lesson ideas for this book go to *ioulessons.com*

We would love to hear your comments, reviews, ideas, and/or lessons for MY IOU LIFE SHIP!
Email us at lessons@iouliving.com.

Learn about the *12 Essential Life Anchors*™
to help keep your Life Ship on Course!

The bestselling book *IOU Life Leadership* available at
iouliving.com and where all books are sold.

Lightning Source UK Ltd.
Milton Keynes UK
UKRC031029120123
415234UK00001B/3